PORCH

Please return / renew by date shown.
You can renew it at:
norlink.norfolk.gov.uk
or by telephone: 0344 800 8006
Please have your library card & PIN ready

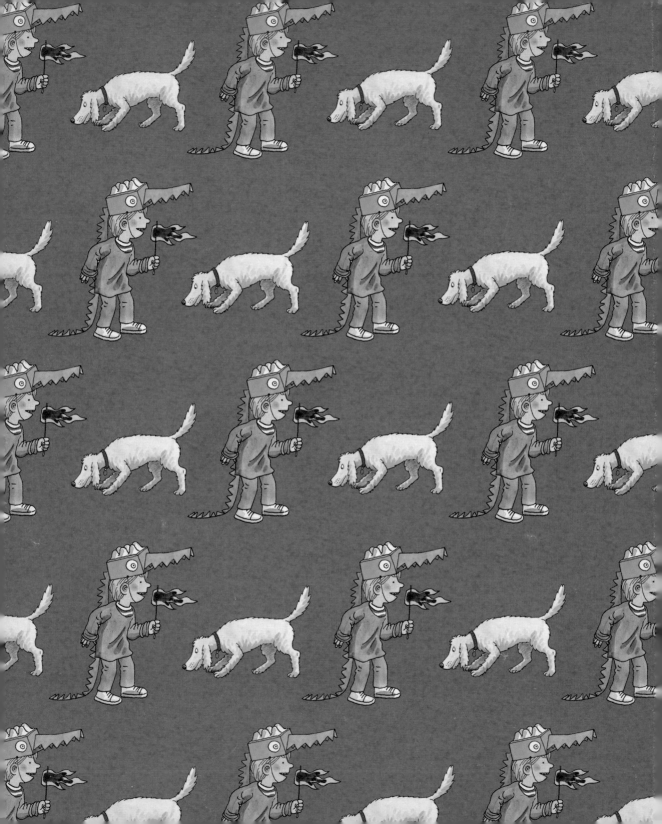

This book belongs to ...

....

OXFORD
UNIVERSITY PRESS

Great Clarendon Street, Oxford, OX2 6DP,
United Kingdom

Oxford University Press is a department of the University of Oxford.
It furthers the University's objective of excellence in research, scholarship,
and education by publishing worldwide. Oxford is a registered trade mark of
Oxford University Press in the UK and in certain other countries

ISBN: 978-0-19-273434-1

5 7 9 10 8 6 4

Typeset in Edbaskerville

Paper used in the production of this book is a natural, recyclable product made
from wood grown in sustainable forests. The manufacturing process conforms
to the environmental regulations of the country of origin.

Acknowledgements;
Series Editors: Kate Ruttle, Annemarie Young

READ WITH
Biff,
Chip &
Kipper

Dragon Danger
and Other Stories

Wet Feet 6

The Red Coat 28

Dragon Danger 50

The Spaceship 72

OXFORD
UNIVERSITY PRESS

Tips for Reading Together

Children learn best when reading is fun.

- Talk about the title and the picture on page 7.
- Identify the letter pattern *ee* in the title and talk about the sound it makes when you read it.
- Look at the *ee* words on page 8. Say the sounds in each word and then say the word (e.g. *f-ee-t, feet*).
- Read the story then find the words with *ee*.
- Talk about the story and do the fun activity at the end of the book.

Children enjoy re-reading stories and this helps to build their confidence.

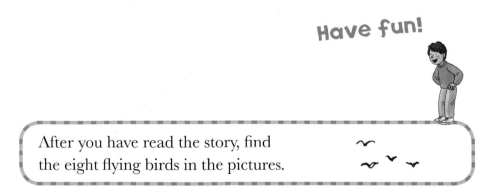

Have fun!

After you have read the story, find the eight flying birds in the pictures.

The main sound practised in this book is 'ee' as in *deep*.

For more hints and tips on helping your child become a successful and enthusiatic reader look at our website www.oxfordowl.co.uk.

Wet Feet

Written by Roderick Hunt
Illustrated by Alex Brychta

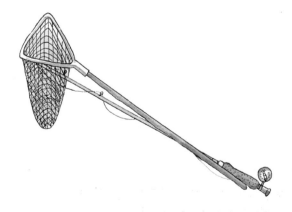

OXFORD
UNIVERSITY PRESS

Read these words

deep   feed

feel   need

reel   weed

feet   eel

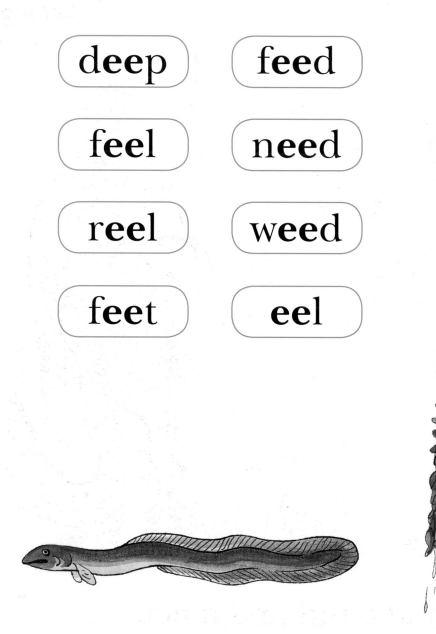

Wilf had a rod and a net.

Wilf and Dad got to the river.

"We can fish in that bit,"
said Dad.

"Let's get fishing," said Wilf.

"Let's feed the fish," said Dad.

"I can feel a fish," said Wilf.

"Reel it in, then," said Dad.

It was not a fish. It was lots of weeds.

"I can feel a fish," said Dad.

Dad got his feet wet.

Wilf got his feet wet.

"Get the net," said Dad.

It was an eel.

Dad let the eel go.

"We got an eel and wet feet," said
Wilf. "But no fish."

Talk about the story

Where did Wilf and Dad go fishing?

What did they catch?

How did they get wet feet?

What do you like doing at the weekend?

Jumbled letters

Make the *ee* words.

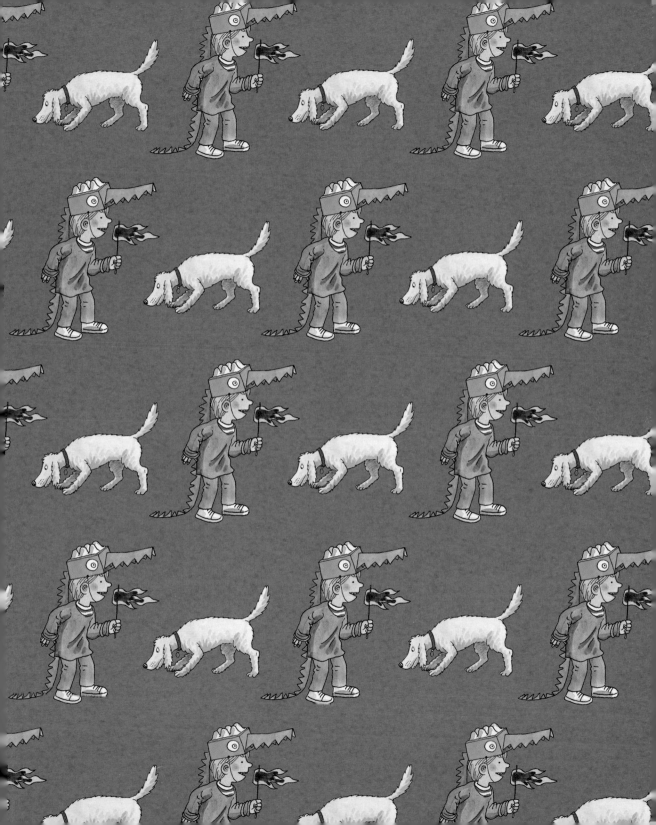

Tips for Reading Together

Children learn best when reading is fun.

- Talk about the title and the picture on page 29.
- Identify the letter pattern *oa* in the title and talk about the sound it makes when you read it.
- Look at the *oa* and *oy* words on page 30. Say the sounds in each word and then say the word (e.g. *s-oa-p, soap*).
- Read the story then find the words with *oa*.
- Talk about the story and do the fun activity at the end of the book.

Children enjoy re-reading stories and this helps to build their confidence.

Have fun!

After you have read the story, find eight stars in the pictures.

The main sound practised in this book is 'oa' as in *coat*.

For more hints and tips on helping your child become a successful and enthusiatic reader look at our website www.oxfordowl.co.uk.

The Red Coat

Written by Roderick Hunt
Illustrated by Nick Schon,
based on the original characters
created by Roderick Hunt and Alex Brychta

OXFORD
UNIVERSITY PRESS

Read these words

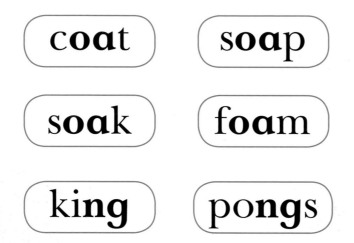

coat　　soap

soak　　foam

king　　pongs

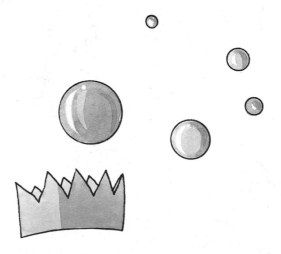

Chip was a king.

I am King Chip.

"I am a king," Chip said to Mum.

"I need a king's coat," he said.

A red coat.

Mum took Chip to a shop.

Chip put on a red coat.

The coat had an odd smell.

"Yuk. It smells odd," said Chip.

Chip put the coat in the tub.

"It can soak in the tub," he said.

What a lot of foam.

Dad had a load of washing.

Chip put the coat in.

Dad's washing was red.

"Look at my washing," said Dad.

Chip was upset.

"But look at the coat," said Mum.

"He is the red king," said Mum.

Talk about the story

Why did Chip want a red coat?

What was wrong with the coat?

Why did Dad's washing turn red?

What do you like dressing up as?

Spot the difference

Find the five differences in the two pictures of Chip.

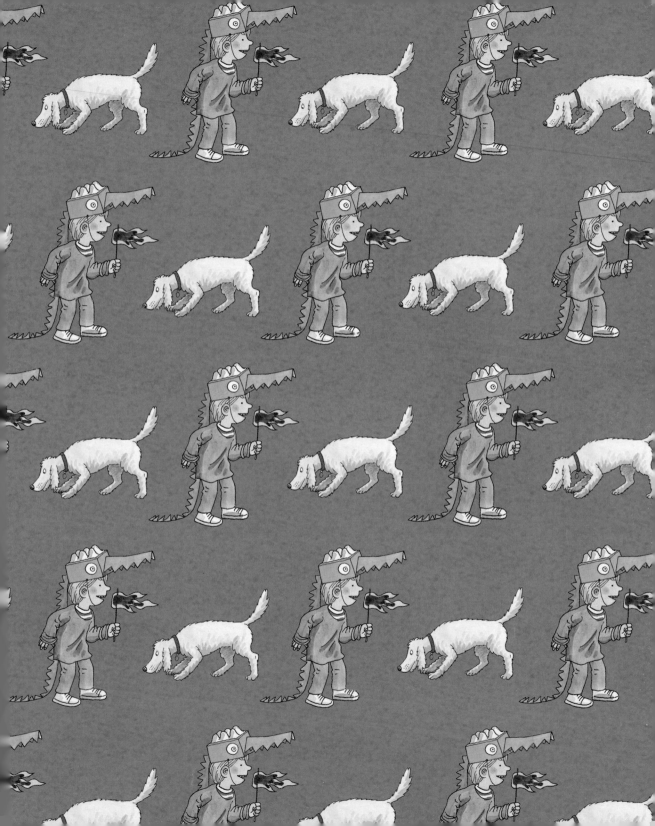

Tips for Reading Together

Children learn best when reading is fun.

- Talk about the title and the picture on page 51.

- Discuss what you think the story might be about.

- Read the story together, inviting your child to read with you.

- Give lots of praise as your child reads with you, and help them when necessary.

- If they get stuck, try reading the first sound or syllable of the word, or read the whole sentence. Focus on the meaning.

- Re-read the story later, encouraging your child to read as much of it as they can.

Children enjoy re-reading stories and this helps to build their confidence.

Have fun!

After you have read the story, find the 10 different reptiles hidden in the pictures.

This book includes these useful common words:
saw   said   came   out   she

For more hints and tips on helping your child become a successful and enthusiastic reader look at our website www.oxfordowl.co.uk.

Dragon
Danger

Written by Cynthia Rider,
based on the original characters
created by Roderick Hunt and Alex Brychta
Illustrated by Alex Brychta

OXFORD
UNIVERSITY PRESS

Floppy was dreaming about
dragons.

Floppy saw a baby dragon with
its mother.

The mother dragon saw Floppy.

"Go away," she roared.

The dragon roared again and
flapped her wings.

She flew at Floppy.

"Oh help!" he said.

WHOOSH! Flames came out of the dragon's mouth.

Floppy hid, but the
dragon saw him.

Floppy ran onto a bridge.
WHOOSH! Flames came
out of the dragon's mouth again.

"Help!" said Floppy.

"The bridge is on fire."

Floppy ran back across
the bridge.

He ran past a rock and saw the
baby dragon again.

The mother dragon roared at
Floppy. She flew up onto a
high rock.

Oh no! The rock started to fall.

CRASH! The rock fell
down . . .

but Floppy pulled the baby
dragon out of danger.
"Phew! Just in time," he said.

What a brave dog!

Talk about the story

Why did the mother dragon roar at Floppy?

Why couldn't Floppy hide from the dragon?

How do you think Floppy felt when the rock started to fall?

What other dragon stories do you know?

A maze

Help Floppy find his way out of the dragon's maze.

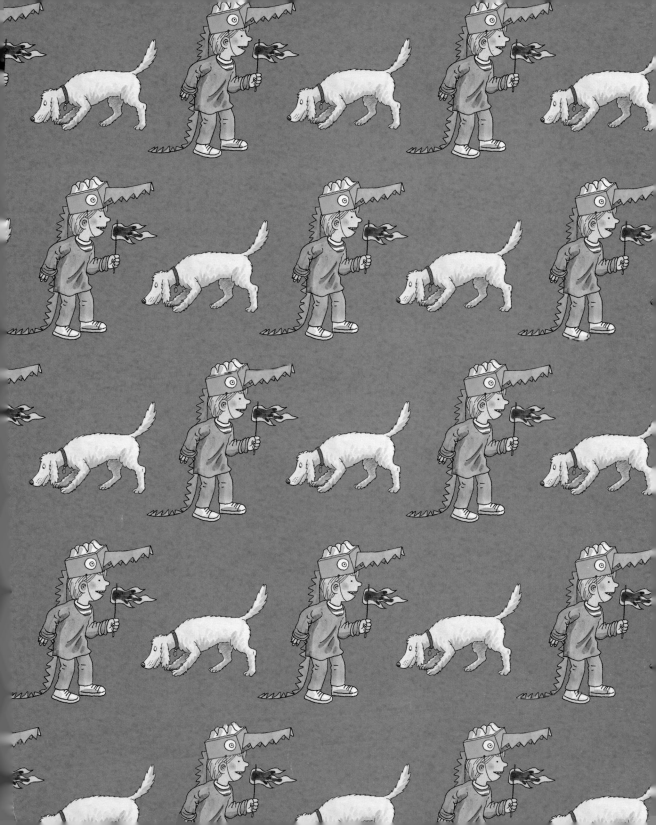

Tips for Reading Together

Children learn best when reading is fun.

- Talk about the title and the picture on page 73.
- Discuss what you think the story might be about.
- Read the story together, inviting your child to read with you.
- Give lots of praise as your child reads with you, and help them when necessary.
- If they get stuck, read the first sound or syllable of the word, or read the whole sentence. Focus on the meaning.
- Re-read the story later, encouraging your child to read as much of it as they can.

Children enjoy re-reading stories and this helps to build their confidence.

Have fun!

Find these 10 space bugs hidden in the pictures.

This book includes these useful common words:
said   what   help   them

For more hints and tips on helping your child become a successful and enthusiastic reader look at our website www.oxfordowl.co.uk.

The Spaceship

Written by Roderick Hunt
Illustrated by Alex Brychta

OXFORD
UNIVERSITY PRESS

Floppy went to sleep and
he began to dream.

A spaceship landed.

"Wow!" said Kipper.

"A real spaceship!"

An alien came out.

"I am Zig," he said.

"And this is my dog, Zog."

"Let's go into space," said Zig.

"Oh yes!" said Kipper.

"Oh no!" said Floppy.

WHOOSH! The spaceship
took off. It flew up into space.

"What's that?" said Kipper.

"Oh no!" shouted Zig. "Fireballs!"

WHOOSH! Suddenly, there were fireballs all around them.

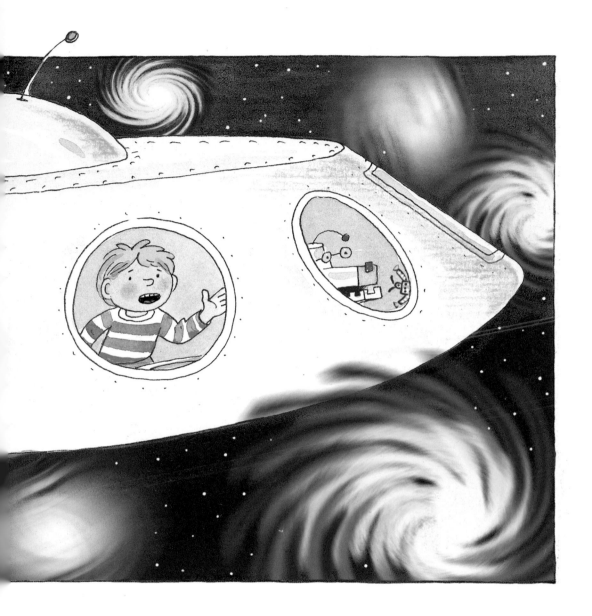

"Help!" shouted Zog.

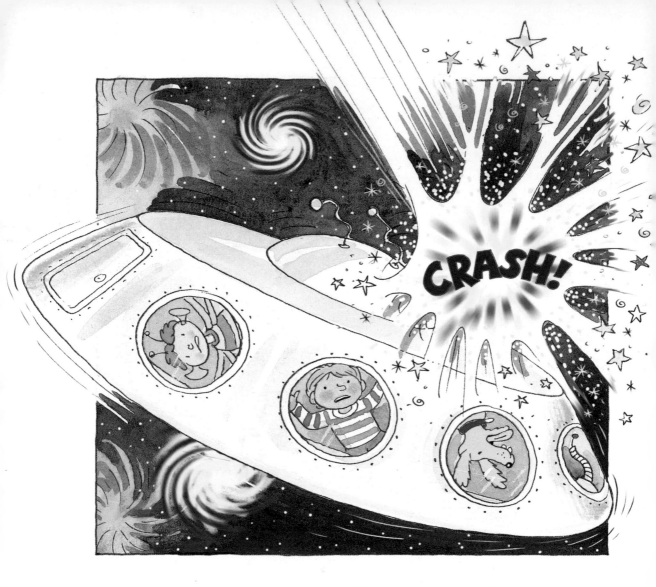

CRASH! A fireball hit them.
The spaceship began to
spin round.

Zig and Kipper bumped heads.

"Oh my head!" groaned Kipper.

"Oh my head!" groaned Zig.

Floppy saw a very big fireball.
It was going to hit them!

"Help!" said Floppy.

"We're in danger!" shouted Zog.

"I don't know what to do."

"I know what to do," said Floppy.
"I can fly the spaceship."

ZOOM! Floppy flew the
spaceship out of danger.
"Phew! Just in time," he said.

"Well done, Space Dog Floppy,"
said Zig. "You saved us!"

Talk about the story

Why did Floppy dream about space?

How did Floppy feel about being in space?

Why did Floppy have to take control of the spaceship? How did he know what to do?

Where do spaceships go in space? Where would you like to go?

91

A maze

Help the spaceship find its way through the fireballs to the Earth.

Read with Biff, Chip and Kipper
The UK's best-selling home reading series

Phonics

First Stories

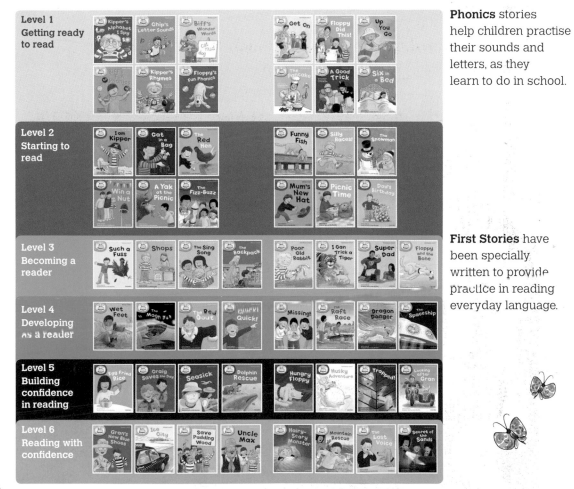

Level	Phonics	First Stories
Level 1 Getting ready to read	Kipper's Alphabet I Spy · Chip's Letter Sounds · Biff's Wonder Words · Kipper's Rhymes · Floppy's Fun Phonics	Get On · Floppy Did This! · Up You Go · The Pancake · A Good Trick · Six in a Bed
Level 2 Starting to read	I am Kipper · Cat in a Bag · The Red Hen · Win a Nut · A Yak at the Picnic · The Fizz-Buzz	Funny Fish · Silly Races! · The Snowman · Mum's New Hat · Picnic Time · Dad's Birthday
Level 3 Becoming a reader	Such a Fuss · Shops · The Sing Song · The Backpack	Poor Old Rabbit · I Can Trick a Tiger · Super Dad · Floppy and the Bone
Level 4 Developing as a reader	Wet Feet · The Moon Jet · The Day Out · Quick!	Missing! · The Raft Race · Dragon Danger · The Spaceship
Level 5 Building confidence in reading	Egg Fried Rice · Craig Saves the Day · Seasick · Dolphin Rescue	Hungry Floppy · Husky Adventure · Trapped! · Looking after Gran
Level 6 Reading with confidence	Gran's New Blue Shoes · Ice City · Save Pudding Wood · Uncle Max	Hairy-Scary Monster · Mountain Rescue · The Lost Voice · Secret of the Sands

Phonics stories help children practise their sounds and letters, as they learn to do in school.

First Stories have been specially written to provide practice in reading everyday language.

Read with Biff, Chip and Kipper Collections:

Up You Go and Other Stories · Kipper's Rhymes and Other Stories · Six in a Bed and Other Stories · Funny Fish and Other Stories · Picnic Time and Other Stories · The Fizz-Buzz and Other Stories · Floppy and the Bone and Other Stories

I Can Trick a Tiger and Other Stories · The Moon Jet and Other Stories · Dragon Danger and Other Stories · Husky Adventure and Other Stories · Looking After Gran and Other Stories · Hairy-Scary Monster and Other Stories · Secret of the Sands and Other Stories

2 Phonics and 2 First Stories in every collection

Phonics support

Flashcards are a really fun way to practise phonics and build reading skills. **Age 3+**

My Phonics Kit is designed to support you and your child as you practise phonics together at home. It includes stickers, workbooks, interactive eBooks, support for parents and more! **Age 5+**

Read Write Inc. Phonics: A range of fun rhyming stories to support decoding skills. **Age 4+**

Songbirds Phonics: Lively and engaging phonics stories from Children's Laureate, Julia Donaldson. **Age 4+**

Helping your child's learning with free eBooks, essential tips and fun activities

www.oxfordowl.co.uk